Hidden Liz

This is Liz. She has a skill.

I can go dull.
I am hidden!

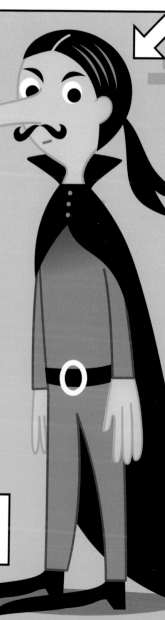

Tish and Tash check ...

No cops!

Liz is hidden.

Tish and Tash go to rob the choc shop.

Choc Shop

I can unlock it!

Click! Click!

5

Tish and Tash smell the chocs.

They rush along to the back of the shop.

9

But then Liz rings the cops.

Be quick!

The cops get Tish and Tash!